Contents

Quiz time!

1. Tom has to be at school by **8.45**a.m. He takes **10** minutes to wash, **12** minutes to dress and **26** minutes to eat breakfast. If it takes him **17** minutes to walk to school, what time should he get up? _____

2. Write in the missing digits in this addition. There are several possible answers.

$$
\begin{array}{c}
5\ \boxed{}\ 6\ 3 \\
+\ 2\ \boxed{}\ 5\ \boxed{} \\
\hline
\boxed{}\ 4\ 1\ 9
\end{array}
$$

3. Write in the missing digits in this subtraction.

$$
\begin{array}{c}
9\ 4\ \boxed{}\ 2 \\
-\ 3\ \boxed{}\ 4\ \boxed{} \\
\hline
\boxed{}\ 6\ 8\ 6
\end{array}
$$

4. Solve the riddle to find the numbers to open the bank vault.

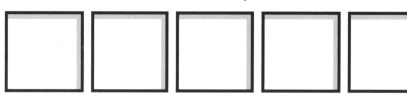

   There is a **2** in the thousands place.

   The digit in the tens place is four times the digit in the thousands place.

   The digit in the hundreds place is half the digit in the tens place.

   The digit in the units place is the next prime number after **5**.

   The final digit is twice the units digit less **5**.

5. Use the digits **9**, **8**, **7**, **6**, **5**, **4**, **3**, **2**, **1**, in the order given, and some addition signs to form a calculation that sums to a total of **99**. Hint: you may need to make some two-digit numbers.

6. Use trial and error to answer the following question.

   Take a one-digit number.

   Multiply it by **3**. Add **8**. Divide by **2**. Subtract **6**.

   You should have the number you started with.

   This will only work with one number. What is it? _____

Schofield&Sims

KS2 Problem Solving 4

Name

Schofield&Sims

KS2 Problem Solving Book 4

written by Ann Montague-Smith

Notes for the teacher

This book contains enrichment activities that are suitable for Year 6 children, which give them the opportunity to become more confident in solving maths problems. The multi-step problems provided will encourage the children to develop specific problem-solving skills, including:

- making jottings in order to help them with calculation
- using a calculator appropriately
- solving problems set in real-life contexts, with realistic numbers.

The main learning objectives for each activity are given on the Contents page; these are taken from the National Strategy Primary Framework for Mathematics. Aspects of all seven strands are covered (Year 6 unless otherwise indicated), although it has not been possible to cover every objective in this workbook. Use the Contents page to find work that is appropriate both for individuals and for groups. Children will find it useful to have rough paper for jottings, and for some questions you may wish to ask them to set out their workings, with solutions, in full. This will enable you to assess whether they can make efficient choices about the method of achieving the solution.

Encourage the children to explain to a work partner, and to the class, how they have solved the problem they are working on. Ask them to consider whether there might be a more effective method, and to explore ways of extending the problem – perhaps by writing a new problem, based on the original material and their solution, for others to try.

Published by **Schofield & Sims Ltd**, Dogley Mill Fenay Bridge, Huddersfield HD8 0NQ, UK (tel 01484 607080; web www.schofieldandsims.co.uk)

First published in 2008
Copyright © Schofield and Sims Limited 2008

This edition, with revisions, first published in 2013. Second impression 2013

Author: **Ann Montague-Smith**

British Library Cataloguing in Publication Data
A catalogue record for this book is available from the British Library.

Design by **Ledgard Jepson, Sheffield**

Printed in the UK by Wyndeham Gait Ltd., Grimsby, Lincolnshire

ISBN 978 07217 1138 6

Family fractions

1. The ten-year-olds from the Smith, Jones and Khan families each chose one of these fractions.

$\frac{9}{16}$ $\frac{3}{8}$ $\frac{3}{4}$

Change the fractions to decimal fractions and place them on this number line.

0   1

2. Mr Jones said to his son, 'Which would you rather have: $\frac{7}{10}$ or $\frac{8}{9}$ of £**50**?'

a. Which fraction represents the larger amount of money?

b. What is the difference between the two amounts of money?

£

3. The children in the Smith family wear fifths fractions on their T-shirts. The children in the Jones family wear eighths fractions on their T-shirts. The children in the Khan family wear sevenths fractions on their T-shirts.

a. Sort these fractions into the correct family. To show your choice, write the first letter of the family name beneath each fraction.

$\frac{12}{21}$ $\frac{6}{15}$ $\frac{8}{14}$ $\frac{12}{32}$ $\frac{4}{7}$ $\frac{20}{50}$ $\frac{24}{64}$

$\frac{16}{28}$ $\frac{9}{24}$ $\frac{6}{16}$ $\frac{4}{10}$ $\frac{32}{56}$ $\frac{10}{25}$

b. Find the simplest form of the fractions for each family and write it in the box on the T-shirt.

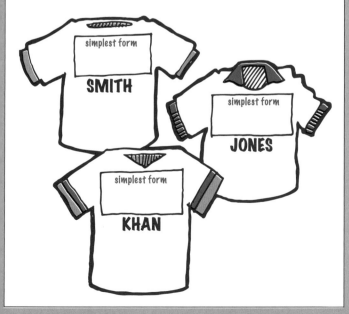

simplest form

SMITH

simplest form

JONES

simplest form

KHAN

4. Mr Smith decided to share £**100** between his four children. He gave the oldest $\frac{2}{5}$ of the money. To the second oldest he gave $\frac{2}{7}$ of the money. To the second youngest he gave $\frac{2}{9}$ of the money. How much money was left for the youngest child?

£ _____

5. Mr Khan offered his three children a choice: $\frac{9}{10}$ of a pizza shared between them or a quarter of a pizza each.

a. Which way gives the larger piece of pizza for each child?

b. What fraction of the total pizza would the larger piece for one child be?

6. Mrs Jones suggested to her five children that they run a distance of **500** metres between them. The youngest child ran $\frac{1}{8}$ of the way. The second youngest ran $\frac{3}{16}$ of the way. The third child ran $\frac{1}{4}$ of the way. The second oldest had a sprained ankle so did not run. How far did the oldest child have to run?

_____

Planet Targ

The people of Targ decided to build their roads using a grid system.

Route Planner

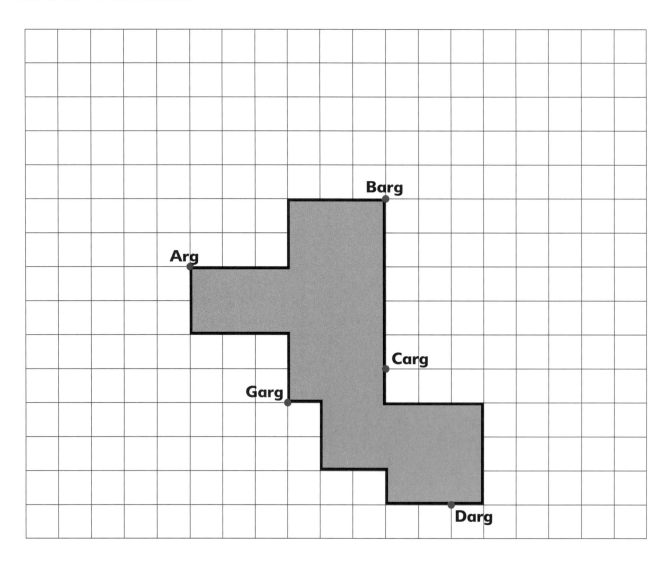

The side of each small square represents **7** km.

> **8 kilometres** is approximately **5 miles**.
> **1 litre** is approximately **1.75 pints**.

1. Following the road in a clockwise direction, what is the distance in kilometres between Arg and Barg? _____

2. Some Targians go from Arg to Darg using a clockwise route. How far is this in kilometres? _____

3. Other Targians go from Arg to Darg using an anti-clockwise route. How far is this in kilometres? _____

4. Travelling anti-clockwise, how much further is it from Garg to Carg than Garg to Darg? _____

Most Targians prefer to use imperial measures.

5. All Targians have to go for a run on Sunday mornings. They run from Carg to Darg. How far is that in miles? _____

6. How far would it be in miles to drive along the entire road, starting and finishing in Darg? _____

7. Targ imports plum juice from Planet Ongo. Ongoians use metric units so they bottle plum juice in two-litre containers. What is this in pints? _____

8. Targians buy their milk in nine-pint containers. About how much milk is this in litres? _____

9. The cars on Targ go **60** miles on three pints of fuel. Re-write this sentence changing miles to kilometres and pints to litres.

_____

_____

_____

10. Targians buy soup by the bucket. One bucket holds eight pints. Approximately how much soup is this in litres? _____

Living on Planet Targ

You will need to use a ruler when answering most of the questions on pages 8 and 9.

1. The floor plan of houses on Targ is always made from two identical isosceles triangles placed edge to edge. Draw five different floor plans.

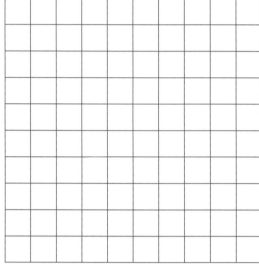

2. Draw two isosceles triangles that touch edge to edge. The final shape must have four right angles and two pairs of parallel sides.

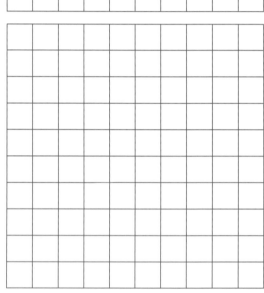

3. What is special about the isosceles triangles needed to make the shape in Question **2**?

4. The houses' floor plans on planet Ongo are built using three identical equilateral triangles placed edge to edge. Draw a floor plan.

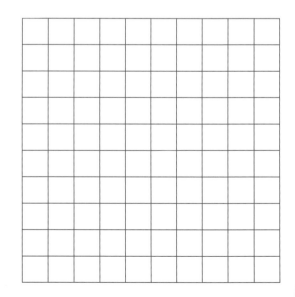

5. All gardens on Targ have a plan of a quadrilateral.

   a. Forty per cent of Targians like their garden to have at least one pair of parallel sides.

   b. Forty per cent of Targians prefer their garden to have a pair of perpendicular sides.

   c. Ten per cent of Targians want both a pair of parallel sides and at least one right angle.

   Sketch two examples of each type of garden and label them **a**, **b** or **c**.

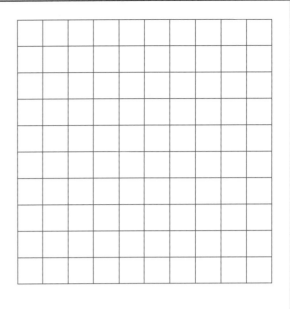

6. Ten per cent of Targians like a garden plan that is a quadrilateral with diagonals that intersect at their mid-point. Sketch an example, marking in the diagonals.

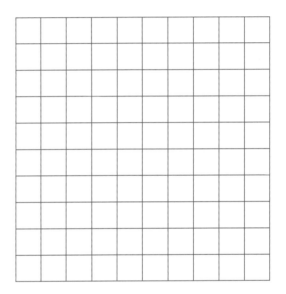

7. Flower beds on Targ are always planned as a regular polygon with at least two sets of parallel sides. Sketch three examples and write the name of each shape.

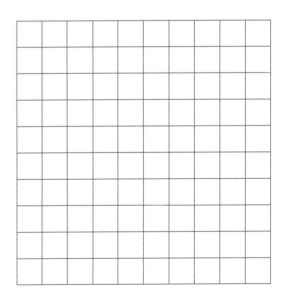

The main chance

Write true or false under these statements.

1.
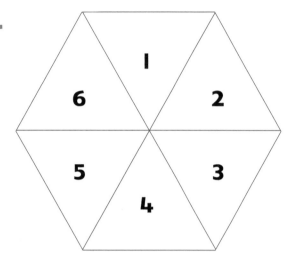

I have an even chance of spinning an odd number.

_____

2.
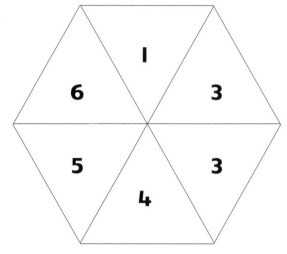

I have an even chance of spinning an odd number.

_____

Katie puts six counters into a bag.
Three are green.
Two are red.
One is blue.

3. What is her chance of taking out a green counter? _____

4. What is her chance of taking out a red or blue counter? _____

5. Which colour of counter is least likely to be drawn? _____

6. Katie adds five blue counters and one green counter.

   a. Which colour of counter is most likely to be drawn? _____

   b. Which colour of counter is least likely to be drawn? _____

Be quick!

Time how long it takes you to complete these problems.

1. Write the answer to **5 x 4** in the first box. This number starts the second question. The answer to that goes in the second box, and so on.

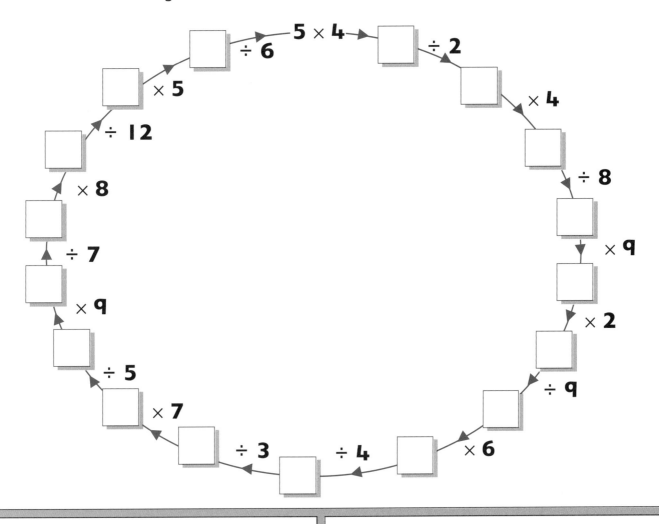

2. I am a square number.
   My factors are greater
   than **6** and less than **8**.
   What am I? _____

3. I am a square number, smaller
   than **150**, larger than **100**.
   The sum of my digits is **9**.
   What number multiplied
   by itself made me? _____

4. I am a square with
   sides of **9** cm.
   What is my area? _____

5. I am made from two equal
   squares placed side by side.
   Their total area is **72** cm².
   What is the length of one
   side of one of my squares? _____

6. All my sides are the
   same length.
   I have one more side
   than an octagon.
   What am I? _____

Write how long you took to
do these. _____

Rainy days

1. Look at this rainfall frequency chart carefully. It gives the rainfall per month in millimetres for England, Scotland, Northern Ireland and Wales.

	J	F	M	A	M	J	J	A	S	O	N	D	Total
England	54	40	37	37	46	45	57	59	49	57	64	48	
Scotland	57	42	51	41	51	51	57	65	67	65	63	58	
Northern Ireland	86	58	67	53	60	63	64	80	85	88	78	78	
Wales	108	72	63	65	76	63	89	97	99	109	116	108	
Total													

   a. Find the total rainfall for each country and write this in the chart.

   b. Complete the rainfall each month for the United Kingdom and write this in the chart.

2. Which country has the greatest rainfall? _____

3. Which country has the lowest rainfall? _____

4. What is the mean rainfall for each country?

   England _____

   Scotland _____

   Northern Ireland _____

   Wales _____

5. Find the range for the rainfall for each country.

   England _____

   Scotland _____

   Northern Ireland _____

   Wales _____

6. Draw a bar chart to show the rainfall for each month in the United Kingdom. Complete the axes labels and the title boxes.

7. a. Which is the wettest month in the UK? _____

b. Is this the same as the wettest month in England? _____

c. Write some sentences to explain how you worked this out.

_____

_____

Problem medley

1. Tim travelled from home to town by bus. His fare was **£2·00**. How far did he travel if the fare is **£1·20** for the first half a kilometre and **20**p for each additional **250** metres?

2. The peel of a banana is about $\frac{1}{8}$ of the total weight of a banana. If you buy **2** kg of bananas at **90**p a kilo, how much are you paying for the banana peel?

3. Chung bought eight T-shirts from the local cash-and-carry as birthday presents for his cousins. The T-shirts were **£5·20** each. An additional **$17\frac{1}{2}$%** was added at the check-out. How much change did he have from **£100**?

4. If you saved **£2** on January 1st, **£4** on February 1st, **£6** on March 1st, and so on, how much would you save in one year?

5. A supermarket has parking for **2000** cars. **120** of the spaces are for people with disabilities and $\frac{1}{10}$ are for parents with children. On Tuesday **80** disabled spaces and **70** parent and child spaces were taken. Altogether the car park was **30%** full. How many cars were parked in spaces not reserved for the disabled or parents with children?

6. Lucy decided to put rabbit-proof fencing around her vegetable plot. The plot measured **10** m x **20** m. If the posts for the fencing were placed **2** m apart, how many posts were used?

Pull-out Answers

Page 4

1. **7.40**am or **07.40**

2.
```
  5263        5163        5463        5963
+ 2156      + 2256      + 2956      + 2456
  ----        ----        ----        ----
  7419        7419        8419        8419

  5863        5563        5763        5663
+ 2556      + 2856      + 2656      + 2756
  ----        ----        ----        ----
  8419        8419        8419        8419
```

3.
```
  9432
- 3746
  ----
  5686
```

4. **92 487**

5. **9 + 8 + 7 + 65 + 4 + 3 + 2 + 1**
   or **9 + 8 + 7 + 6 + 5 + 43 + 21**

6. **4**

Page 5

1. **0.5625   0.375   0.75**
   0.375   0.5625   0.75

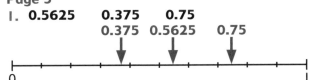

The exact positioning of these numbers is not important but the numbers must be correct and in the correct order.

2. a. **8/9 of £50**   b. **£9.44**

3. a. Smith: $\frac{4}{10}$; $\frac{6}{15}$; $\frac{10}{25}$; $\frac{20}{50}$

   Jones: $\frac{6}{16}$; $\frac{9}{24}$; $\frac{12}{32}$; $\frac{24}{64}$

   Khan: $\frac{4}{7}$; $\frac{8}{14}$; $\frac{12}{21}$; $\frac{16}{28}$; $\frac{32}{56}$

   b. simplest forms: Smith $\frac{2}{5}$, Jones $\frac{3}{8}$, Khan $\frac{4}{7}$

4. **£9.21**

5. a. $\frac{9}{10}$ b. $\frac{3}{10}$

6. **218.75** m

Page 7

1. **56** km
2. **147** km
3. **105** km
4. **56** km
5. **35** miles
6. **157·5** miles
7. **3·5** pints
8. **5** litres
9. The cars on Targ go **96** km on **1·7** litres of fuel.
10. **4·5** litres

Page 8

1. Here are three examples.

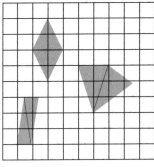

2. Here is an example.

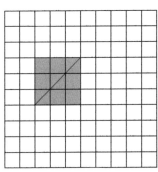

3. They must be identical right-angled triangles.

4. Here is an example.

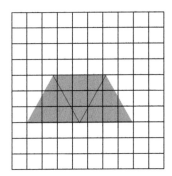

Page 9

5. Here are two examples of each.
   a.
   b.

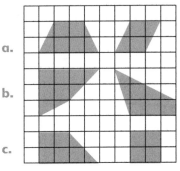

   c.

6. Here are three examples.

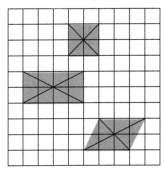

7. Any regular polygon with an even number of sides for example square, hexagon, octagon.

Page 10

1. True

2. False

3. $\frac{1}{2}$ or even

4. $\frac{1}{2}$ or even

5. Blue

6. a. Blue   b. Red

Page 11

1. 5×4→20÷2→10×4→40÷8→5×9→45×2→90÷9→
10×6→60÷4→15÷3→5×7→35÷5→7×9→63÷7→
9×8→72÷12→6×5→30

2. **49**

3. **12**

4. **81** cm²

5. **6** cm

6. Nonagon

Page 12

1. a. **593; 668; 860; 1065**
   b. **305; 212; 218; 196; 233; 222; 267; 301; 300;
   319; 321; 292**

2. **Wales**

3. **England**

4. England: **49.42** mm
   Scotland: **55.67** mm
   Northern Ireland: **71.67** mm
   Wales: **88.75** mm

5. England: **27** mm
   Scotland: **26** mm
   Northern Ireland: **35** mm
   Wales: **53** mm

Page 13

6.

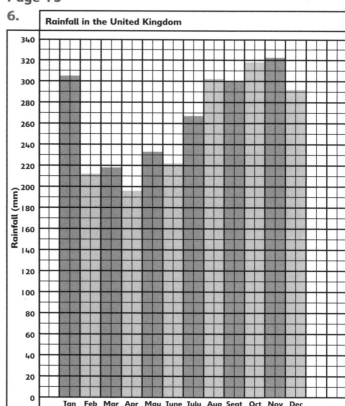

7. a. November   b. Yes   c. Pupil's explanation

Page 14

1. **1·5** km
2. **22.5**p
3. **£51·12**
4. **£156**
5. **450**
6. **30**

Page 15

7. **49**
8. **£528**

Page 16

1. Measure the depth of the book; count the number of
   pages and use calculator to find the average depth
   per page.

2. a. **224**   b. **221**   c. **225**

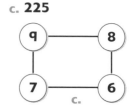

3. Five from **1, 7, 11, 13, 77, 91, 143, 1001**

4. **3776**

Page 17

1. **(4, 4)**
2. **(4, 5); (1, 4)**

3.

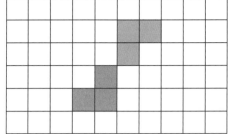

4.

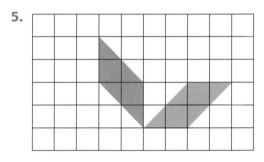

5.

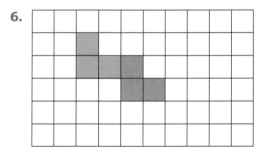

6.

Page 18

1.

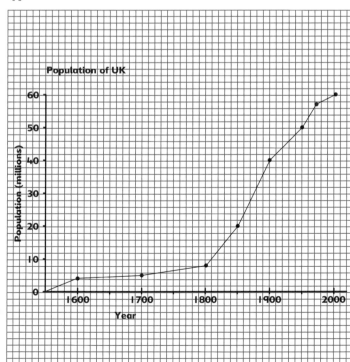

2. 1851–1901
The graph is steepest between these years.

Page 19

3.

	1901	2001	2011	2051
Male	18·49	28·81	29·85	31·67
Female	19·75	31·00	31·17	33·78
Total	38·24	59·81	61·02	65·45

4. **4·43** million

5. Females

6.

	Land area in sq.km	No. of people in each sq.km	Population
England	130 281	383	49 897 623
Northern Ireland	13 576	125	1 697 000
Scotland	77 925	65	5 065 125
Wales	20 732	142	2 943 944
Total	242 514		59 603 692

7. **246**

Page 20

1. Perimeter: **32** m
Area: **56** m²

2. Perimeter: **32** m
Area: **48** m²

3. **30** m

4. **50** m²

5. **22** m

6. **24** m²

7. **26** m²
Pupil's explanation

Page 21

1. **36**

2. **286** and **287**

3. **13.44**

4. **20**

5. a. **64**p   b. **I**p+**2**p etc   c. **2**p

6. **8**p.m or **20.00**

Page 22
1. **3597**

2 **500**

3. **£1106**

4. **8**

5. **12**

6.

6	–I	4
I	3	5
2	7	0

Page 23
1. Radio Mart **£57·38**
   Talk Shop: **£57·00**
   talktoyou.co.uk: **£56·29**
   speaktogether.co.uk: **£65·33**

2. talktoyou.co.uk

3. **£52·09**

4. No, because Radio Mart special deal is cheapest price.

Page 24
1. **60**

2. **150°**

3. a. **45°**   b. **135°**

4. **60°**

5. a. **£132**   b. **£11**

Page 25
1.

	Florida Fun	USA Galore	Book and Go!	Eagle Express	Florida and more
Total cost	2916	3366	3578	3076	3246

2. Range: **£662**
   Median: **£3246**
   Mean: **£3236·40**

3. Florida Fun

4. **£2478·60**

Page 26
5. **£664**

6. **£174**

7. **£24 200**

8. **£74·46**

9. **£297·85**

10. **3·32** tonnes

Page 27
1.

2. **123; 645; 876**

3. **948; 1368; 6642**

4. The toy from the toy shop.

5. **120; 8472; 239 976**
   Pupil's explanation

7. Emiko asked the girls at her party to take some strawberries from a basket. The first girl took one strawberry, the second girl took three, the third girl took five, and so on until each of the seven guests had taken some strawberries. Now the basket was empty. How many strawberries were there in the basket to start with?

8. Mrs Ho wants to carpet her living room which is a rectangle measuring **5** m × **6** m.

How much will the carpet cost if she buys it in the sale?

Calculator calculating

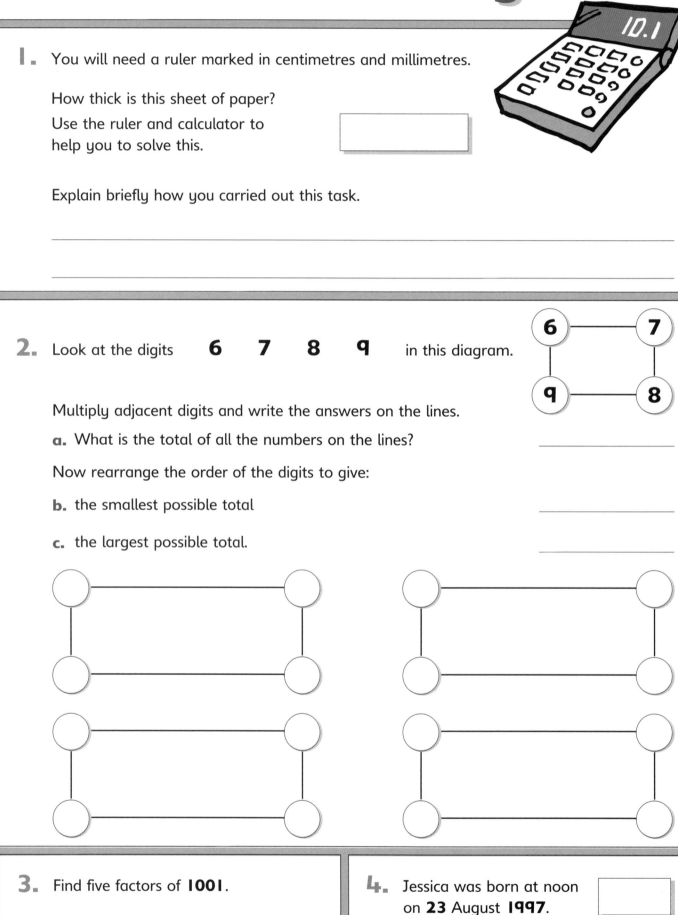

1. You will need a ruler marked in centimetres and millimetres.

   How thick is this sheet of paper?
   Use the ruler and calculator to
   help you to solve this.

   Explain briefly how you carried out this task.

   _____

   _____

2. Look at the digits   **6   7   8   9**   in this diagram.

   Multiply adjacent digits and write the answers on the lines.

   a. What is the total of all the numbers on the lines?   _____

   Now rearrange the order of the digits to give:

   b. the smallest possible total   _____

   c. the largest possible total.   _____

3. Find five factors of **1001**.

4. Jessica was born at noon
   on **23** August **1997**.

   For how many days has she been alive
   at noon on **25** December **2007**?

Shapes and mirrors

1. A, B, C are three corners of a parallelogram.

Write the coordinates of the fourth corner. _____

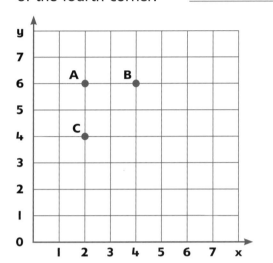

2. Plot (**2**, **1**) and (**5**, **2**). The line joining these two points is one side of a square. Write the coordinates of the other two points. _____

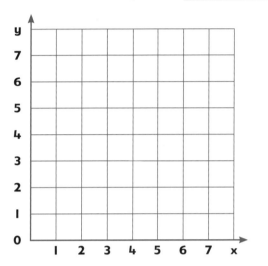

3. This shape is rotated **180°** clockwise about point A. Draw its new position on the grid.

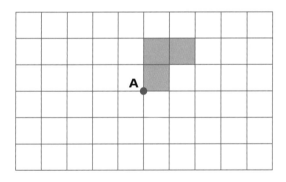

4. Draw the reflection of this shape.

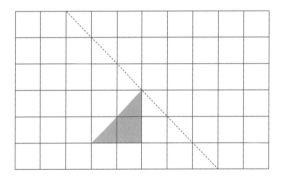

5. This shape is rotated **90°** anti-clockwise about point A. Draw its new position.

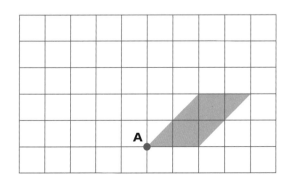

6. Draw this shape after it has been translated two squares to the East and one square to the South.

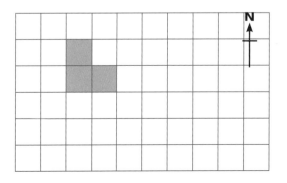

Population explosion

1. These are the population figures for the UK rounded to the nearest million people from **1600** to **2005**.

1600	1700	1801	1851	1901	1951	1971	2005
4	5	8	20	40	50	57	60

Plot these figures in a graph.

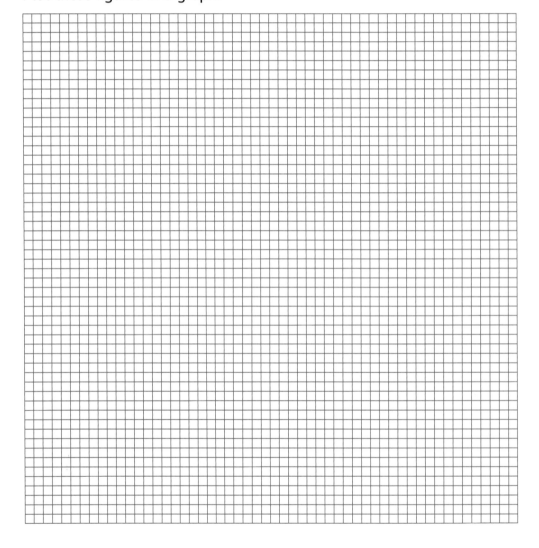

2. Between which years do you think that the population grew fastest?

Write a sentence to explain how you worked this out from the graph.

_____

_____

3. Here are some statistics showing a population growth forecast in the UK. The population is shown in millions.

	1901	2001	2011	2051
Male	18·49	28·81		31·67
Female	19·75		31·17	33·78
Total		59·81	61·02	

Complete the table by writing in the missing data.

4. By how much is the population expected to grow between **2011** and **2051**? Write your answer in millions. _____

5. Which is likely to be greater: the population growth for males or the population growth for females between **2011** and **2051**? _____

6. Here are some statistics about the countries of the UK.

	Land area in sq.km	No. of people in each sq.km	Population
England	130 281	383	
Northern Ireland	13 576	125	
Scotland	77 925	65	
Wales	20 732	142	
Total			

Use your calculator to work out the population for each country. Fill in the empty boxes in the 'Population' column. Then work out the total land area in square kilometres and add this figure to the table.

7. Use your answers to Question **6** to work out the mean number of people in each square kilometre in the UK. Round the figure to the nearest whole number.

Parkside School garden

Class **6** decides to plan a new school garden.
Here are some of the plans that the children drew.
Calculate the perimeter and area of each garden.

1.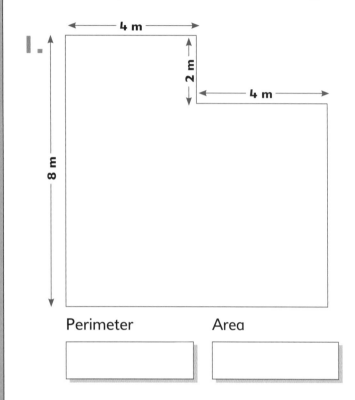

Perimeter

Area

2.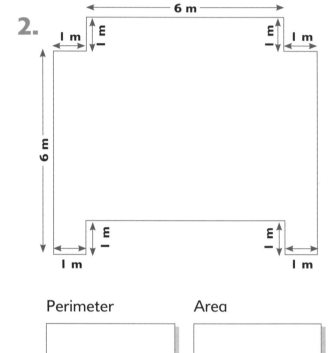

Perimeter

Area

The class chose this simple design for their garden.

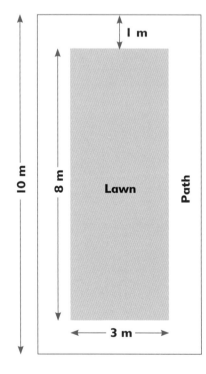

3. What is the perimeter of the outside of the garden?

4. What is the area of the whole garden?

5. What is the perimeter of the lawn?

6. What is the area of the lawn?

7. What is the area of the path?

Write a sentence to explain how you worked this out.

_____

Number puzzles

1. Nikki gave Luke half of her crayons. Luke gave Chelsea half of the crayons that he had received from Nikki. Chelsea kept **12** of the crayons and gave the remaining six to Eve. How many crayons did Nikki give to Luke?

2. The sum of the page numbers on the open pages of a large dictionary is **573**. What are the page numbers?

3. Solve this. Do not use a calculator.

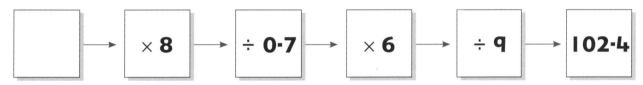

| | → | ✕ **8** | → | ÷ **0·7** | → | ✕ **6** | → | ÷ **9** | → | **102·4** |

4. Sam wrote all the whole numbers between **1** and **100**. How many times did he write the number **2**?

5. Jamie asked if he could have pocket money. His father gave him a choice: either £**1.25** a week, or **1**p on Monday, **2**p on Tuesday, **4**p on Wednesday and so on to Sunday.

    a. How much pocket money would Jamie receive each week using the second payment method?

    b. Which way would give him more pocket money?

    c. How much more would he get?

6. Megan noticed that the number of hours left on Tuesday was $\frac{1}{5}$ of the number of hours already passed. What time was it?

Mixed bag of problems

1. *Luna 2*, a spacecraft, crashed on the surface of the Moon on **14** September **1959**. The first astronauts landed on the Moon on **20** July **1969**. How many days after *Luna 2* crashed did astronauts land on the Moon?

2. Peter earned some money by washing dishes at his dad's café. For every dish he washed he earned **7**p. For every dish he broke he had **25**p deducted from his wages. At the end of the first day he had broken **8** dishes and earned **£33**. How many dishes did he wash up?

3. At Pet Haven Rescue Centre it costs **£4** a day to keep a cat, and **£7** a day to keep a dog. Last week there were **15** cats and **14** dogs at the centre. How much money did Pet Haven need to keep the animals for the whole week?

4. Emma is learning to play the guitar but hates practising. Her teacher, Mrs Thomas, wants Emma to practise for at least **3** hours before her next lesson. If she practises for **5** minutes on day **1**, **10** minutes on day **2**, **15** minutes on day **3**, and so on, for how many days will she need to practise before she can have her next lesson?

5. The average adult's heart beats **103 680** times in a day. The average **10**-year-old's heart beats **120 960** times in a day. How many more beats in **1** minute does the **10**-year-old's heart beat than the adult's heart?

6. Complete this magic square.
   It contains the digits **–1, 0, 1, 2, 3, 4, 5, 6, 7**.
   Remember: columns, rows and diagonals all total to the same number.

6		
	3	
		0

Internet shopping

10.1

Ben wants two walkie talkie radios, one for him and one for Max. Ben likes to make model aeroplanes in his shed at the bottom of the garden but when he is in his shed he never hears Max calling him. Max could use the walkie talkie radio to communicate with Ben.

Here are some prices from the internet for walkie talkie radios.

1. Write in the total price for each internet site.
   VAT is **17.5**%

Radio Mart

Pair of walkie talkie radios   **£45**

+ VAT

Postage and packing   **£4.50**

Total _____

talktoyou.co.uk

Take **£20** off the price today!

Pair of walkie talkie radios   **£70**

Including VAT

Postage and packing   **£6·29**

Total _____

Talk Shop

Special offer **5%** discount today!

Pair of walkie talkie radios   **£60**

Including VAT

Postage and packing included.

Total _____

speaktogether.co.uk

Pair of walkie talkie radios   **£55·60**

+ VAT

Free postage and packing

Total _____

2. Which shop offers best value for money? _____

3. Radio Mart decides to have a special sale and offer **10**% off their price before VAT or postage and packing is added. What is the total now? _____

4. Ben finds another site called radiosforall.com.
   This site offers a pair of radios, including VAT and postage and packing for **£52·99**.

   Do you think Ben will buy these? _____

   Why? _____

Stonebanks chain ferry

1. The ferry is pulled across the river by chains. It carries either **20** cars or **12** lorries. It never carries cars and lorries at the same time and it only ever carries full loads. The ferry made five trips across the river and carried **84** vehicles in total.

How many cars did the ferry carry altogether?

2. The hands of the clock on the ferry are stuck at **5**p.m.

What is the angle between the two hands?

3. One of the cogs that helps to operate the chains on the ferry has eight equal angles around the centre.

a. What is the size of each angle at the centre of the cog?

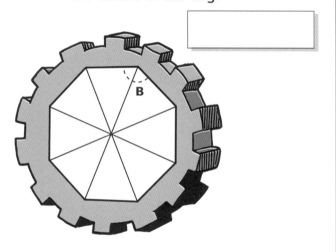

b. What is the size of angle B?

4. The floor shape at the front of the ferry is a trapezium. If angles A and B are each **120°** what is the size of angle C?

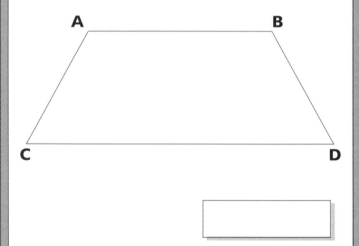

5. The cost of taking one car on a single journey across the river is £**6·60**.

a. How much money does the ferryman take for a full ferry of **20** cars?

b. If the same amount of money for **12** lorries must be taken as for **20** cars, what is the cost for one lorry?

Off to Florida

Mr and Mrs Jones and their two children want to go on holiday to Florida.

Here are the prices in £s from five different holiday companies for the week that they have chosen.

1. Calculate the price for each of these holidays for two adults and two children for one week.

	Florida Fun	USA Galore	Book and Go!	Eagle Express	Florida and more
1 adult	959	1099	1199	1049	1159
1st child	399	579	583	402	429
2nd child	599	589	597	576	499
Total cost					

2. Find the range, median and mean for each total cost of these holidays.

Range

Median

Mean

Mr and Mrs Jones decide to book the cheapest holiday. The travel shop offers them a **15**% discount on the price.

3. Which holiday have they chosen?

4. How much will they pay in total?

5. The family buys five-day tickets to the theme parks.
These cost £**177** for an adult and £**155** for a child.
What is the total cost of the five-day tickets for the Jones' family?

6. Mr Jones wants to take the family to the Space Centre. This costs
£**48** for an adult and £**39** for a child. What is the total cost for
the Jones' family for a visit to the Space Centre?

The flight to Florida is on a plane that holds **325** passengers.
The aeroplane uses approximately **55 000** litres of fuel
from Heathrow to Florida.
The cost of the fuel is about **22**p per litre.

7. How much does the fuel cost for the outward and return journeys?

8. Approximately how much does the fuel cost for one passenger?

9. Approximately how much does the fuel cost for the Jones' family?

The Jones' children investigate the amount of carbon the aeroplane
releases during the journey to Florida and back. They found that it is
about **270** tonnes for a full load of **325** passengers.

10. About how much carbon would be released in the exhaust fumes
for the Jones' family?

Words and numbers

1. Here is a word search. Find the answer to each clue and either highlight the words or circle them with your pencil. Some of the letters are used in more than one word, so take care. Some of the letters are not used at all!

a	l	g	e	b	r	a	n	s	w	e	r	s
d	p	e	r	c	e	n	t	a	g	e	x	e
d	r	p	r	o	p	o	r	t	i	o	n	t
k	e	y	r	u	l	e	r	e	a	s	o	n
a	d	i	s	o	l	u	t	i	o	n	n	x
r	i	n	c	x	x	x	e	t	o	t	a	l
e	c	v	a	c	o	i	n	i	n	e	g	d
a	t	e	l	f	o	r	m	u	l	a	o	i
b	e	r	e	o	d	d	i	a	i	x	n	v
a	r	s	m	n	m	i	n	u	t	e	d	i
r	m	e	i	e	x	s	u	m	r	e	a	s
p	a	i	r	a	x	i	s	x	e	x	t	o
p	e	r	p	e	n	d	i	c	u	l	a	r

The type of answer you get when you round figures in a calculation (11)

_____

Out of 100 (7) _____

The answer to a problem (8)

_____

Subtract (5) _____

At right angles (13)

_____

The number that is divided into another number (7)

_____

A number that has only 1 and itself as factors (5)

_____

Sixty seconds (6) _____

The line of a graph that can be horizontal or vertical (4)

_____

The line and numbers for measuring on a ruler or thermometer, for example (5)

_____

Metric unit of capacity or volume (5)

_____

Nine-angled polygon (7)

_____

Shows how to interpret a graph (3)

_____

Combine quantities to make a total (3)

_____

Facts needed to make a graph (4)

_____

Addition is to subtraction as multiplication is to division (7)

_____

Not even (3) _____

Two (4) _____

Result of a calculation (6)

_____

Collection of numbers or objects that belong together (3)

_____

How much altogether (5)

_____

The next number after nine (3)

_____

The number just after zero (3)

_____

I less than 10 (4)

_____

2. Circle the numbers that are divisible by **3**.
86   123   590   645   876   943

3. Circle the numbers that are divisible by **6**.
92   104   948   1368   6642

4. Three of the latest stuffed toys cost £**123** from the department store. One of these toys costs £**39** from the toy shop. Which is better value?

[_____]

5. Circle the numbers that are divisible by **6** and **4**.

120

964

8472

71 314

234 788

239 976

Write a sentence to explain how you worked this out.

_____

_____

_____

_____

_____

_____

Schofield&Sims

the long-established educational publisher
specialising in maths, English and science materials for schools

Key Stage 2 Problem Solving is a series of graded activity books helping children to sharpen their mathematical skills. It encourages them to apply their maths skills to a range of 'real-life' situations, such as shopping and keeping score in games.

Key Stage 2 Problem Solving Book 4 covers:

- Reflection, translation and rotation of shapes
- Averages (mode, median and mean)
- Metric-imperial conversions
- Percentages and decimal numbers
- Converting fractions (finding a common denominator)
- Probability
- Using a calculator.

This book provides enrichment activities for children who are nearing the end of Key Stage 2 and preparing for the transition to Key Stage 3.

The full range of titles in the series is as follows:

Key Stage 2 Problem Solving Book 1 (for Years 3 and 4)   ISBN 978 07217 0935 2

Key Stage 2 Problem Solving Book 2 (for Years 4 and 5)   ISBN 978 07217 0936 9

Key Stage 2 Problem Solving Book 3 (for Years 5 and 6)   ISBN 978 07217 0937 6

Key Stage 2 Problem Solving Book 4 (for Year 6)   ISBN 978 07217 1138 6

Have you tried **Mental Arithmetic** by Schofield & Sims?
This series helps children to sharpen their calculation skills by using mathematical knowledge to solve one- and two-step number problems.

**For further information and to place your order
visit www.schofieldandsims.co.uk or telephone 01484 607080**

ISBN 978-07217-1138-6

9 780721 711386

Schofield&Sims

Dogley Mill, Fenay Bridge, Huddersfield HD8 0NQ
Phone: 01484 607080 Facsimile: 01484 606815
E-mail: sales@schofieldandsims.co.uk
www.schofieldandsims.co.uk

ISBN 978 07217 1138 6

**£2.95
(Retail price)**

Key Stage 2
Age range 7-11 years